How the Leopard got his Spots

by Rudyard Kipling

Retold by Rosie Dickins

Illustrated by John Joven

Reading consultant: Alison Kelly

Once, the leopard
had no spots at all.

This story tells how
things changed.

Long ago, everyone
lived on the light,
sandy plain.

Then, Zebra and Giraffe found a forest.

Everyone had light, sandy skin.

In the dark, they
grew dark patches.

They hid in
the shadows.

Leopard hunted.

Then the hunters let go.
They were puzzled.

"Why have you
grown patches?"

Zebra and Giraffe took one, two, three steps...

Zebra and Giraffe
were gone!

He wrapped
himself in shadows.

The man held out
a hand.

He made shadowy
fingerprints.

So that's how the
leopard got his spots.

PUZZLES

Puzzle 1

Finish the sentence.

Once, the leopard
had .....

pink spots.

flower pots.

no spots at all.

Puzzle 2

Put the pictures in order.

A

He made shadowy fingerprints.

B

"Now we can hide too."

C

He covered himself in shadows.

Puzzle 3
True or False?

The man
caught
a cold.

The man
caught
Giraffe.

Leopard
caught
a fish.

Puzzle 4

Spot five differences
between the two pictures.

Answers to puzzles

Puzzle 1

Once, the leopard had no spots at all.

Puzzle 2

C

He covered himself in shadows.

A

He made shadowy fingerprints.

B

"Now we can hide too."